Amazing Household Uses of
PEROXIDE

More Than 100 Helpful Household Hints

pil

Publications International, Ltd.

Written by Beth Taylor

Cover images from Getty

Interior photos from Shutterstock.com

Louis Weber, CEO
Publications International, Ltd.
8140 Lehigh Avenue
Morton Grove, Illinois 60053

ISBN: 978-1-4508-9161-5

Manufactured in China.

8 7 6 5 4 3 2 1

Note: This book is for informational purposes and is not intended to provide medical advice. Neither Publications International, Ltd. nor the authors, editors, or publisher takes responsibility for any possible consequences from any treatment, procedure, exercise, dietary modification, action, or applications of the medication or preparation by any person reading or following the information in this book. The publication of this book does not constitute the practice of medicine, and this book does not replace your physician, pharmacist or health-care specialist. Before undertaking any course of treatment or nutritional plan, the authors, editors and publisher advise the reader to check with a physician or other health-care provider.

Contents

THE POWER OF PEROXIDE

Put the versatility and value of hydrogen peroxide to work throughout your home. You can use the simple 3-percent solution of hydrogen peroxide found in the first-aid section of drug and grocery stores as a mild bleaching agent, sanitizer, disinfectant, stain-remover, and more. Whether in the kitchen, the bathroom, or the laundry room, you'll be amazed at what peroxide can do!

Hydrogen peroxide (H_2O_2) is the water molecule (H_2O) with one additional oxygen atom. Because it decomposes into water and oxygen, hydrogen peroxide leaves behind no toxic chemical residue. However, hydrogen peroxide loses strength after it is opened and when it is exposed to air and light. Buy hydrogen peroxide solution in small quantities and store it in a cool, dark place in its original opaque container.

MAKING THE GRADE: HYDROGEN PEROXIDE

In 1818, French chemist Louis-Jacques Thénard isolated hydrogen peroxide, naming it *l'eau oxygénée*, or "oxygenated water." It is found in nature and can also be synthesized. The following grades indicate the percentage of hydrogen peroxide in a solution; the rest is water.

• 3-percent grade is intended for home use and is widely available at drug and grocery stores

• 6-percent grade has added activator; makes effective bleaching agent; used primarily for coloring hair

• 30-percent reagent grade is very corrosive; used in medical research, bio-oxidative therapy, and to intravenously treat numerous diseases

• 35-percent food grade is used by the food industry as a nontoxic disinfectant

• 90-percent grade is a propellant; used by the military and NASA as rocket fuel; highly unstable

The following pages offer more than 100 hydrogen peroxide hints for cleaning, laundering, disinfecting, and more. These are a few things you should know before you continue:

• Whenever hydrogen peroxide is called for, use 3-percent hydrogen peroxide solution.

• Never mix hydrogen peroxide and vinegar in the same container; it could produce a corrosive acid. Using separate bottles of hydrogen peroxide and vinegar in tandem is safe and effective.

• Clearly label the contents of all spray bottles.

• When cleaning with any product, it's best to work in a well-ventilated area away from children and pets.

Kitchen Cleanup

The kitchen is one of the most difficult rooms to keep clean. With an endless supply of spills, drips, and foot traffic, kitchen cleanup can feel like an endless series of tasks. But thanks to peroxide, you don't need a different commercial cleaner to address each problem. An indispensable tool in any kitchen, peroxide can safely tackle nearly all kitchen jobs. Once you discover the versatility and power of peroxide, you can say goodbye to all those commercial cleaners under your sink.

COUNTERTOPS AND OTHER SURFACES

• For a basic countertop cleanser, combine equal parts of 3-percent hydrogen peroxide and water in an unused spray bottle. Spray the solution onto kitchen surfaces and wipe clean. No need to rinse.

MULTIPURPOSE KITCHEN CLEANSER

Try these heated and unheated hydrogen peroxide solutions:

Heated solution:
• Heat ½ cup of hydrogen peroxide in a saucepan to 150°F.
• Pour the warm solution into an empty spray bottle.
• Spray on surfaces immediately.
• Let sit for 1 minute.
• Wipe with a clean cloth or paper towel.

Unheated solution:
• Pour ½ cup of room-temperature hydrogen peroxide into an empty spray bottle.
• Spray onto surfaces.
• Let sit for 10 minutes.
• Wipe with a clean cloth or paper towel.

• Use undiluted 3-percent hydrogen peroxide to sanitize kitchen surfaces. Allow peroxide to stand for 1 minute if heated or 10 minutes if unheated before wiping off. The contact time needed to sanitize depends on whether or not the peroxide solution has been heated.

DOING THE DISHES

• Clean soiled kitchen utensils, cutting instruments, and food containers in a sink of hot, soapy water with 1 cup of hydrogen peroxide. Rinse with water.

• Add a couple of tablespoons of hydrogen peroxide to the dishwasher's regular cycle for dazzling drinking glasses. Do not use hydrogen peroxide as a dishwasher additive for loads with silver or copper items.

• Hydrogen peroxide and vinegar pack a powerful one-two punch against salmonella and other food-borne bacteria. To disinfect kitchen surfaces, prepare two spray bottles. Pour 3-percent hydrogen peroxide into one unused spray bottle. Pour distilled white vinegar into the second empty spray bottle. Use both sprays consecutively—the order doesn't matter—and then wipe clean.

• **Tip:** Never mix hydrogen peroxide and vinegar together in the same container. Keep and store hydrogen peroxide and white vinegar in separate, clearly labeled containers to maximize shelf life and effectiveness.

• For stubborn stains on your food containers or utensils, make a paste of baking soda and 3-percent hydrogen peroxide. Apply the paste to the stained areas. Let sit, then rub or wash off.

• Remove baked-on crud from pots and pans with a paste made of hydrogen peroxide and cream of tartar. Allow the paste to sit, then wipe away.

WATER BOTTLES
• Add about ¼ cup of hydrogen peroxide to a plastic water bottle to clean and refresh it. Swirl the hydrogen peroxide around in the bottle. Fill the remainder with water and leave for several hours. Rinse well with clean water.

CUTTING BOARDS
• To disinfect a plastic cutting board after it's been washed, place it in a solution of hydrogen peroxide and water. Soak for at least 10 minutes. Rinse thoroughly, drain, and let air-dry.

• Disinfect wood cutting boards with hydrogen peroxide and white vinegar. Let each liquid rest on the cutting board for about 10 minutes before rinsing with water.

SINKS AND DRAINS

• Clean stainless steel sinks with a mixture of 3-percent hydrogen peroxide and a little warm water. Allow the solution to sit for a few minutes. Rinse with warm water and wipe clean.

• Pour some hydrogen peroxide down kitchen drainpipes periodically to keep them free of germs and odors.

• Gently brighten white porcelain sinks by filling them with 3-percent hydrogen peroxide solution. Let sit for several minutes, and rinse clean.

• Remove built-up crud on a rubber sink mat by soaking it in the sink. Fill the sink with warm water and about ¼ cup hydrogen peroxide. Soak for at least 10 minutes, drain the sink, and rinse everything thoroughly.

KITCHEN APPLIANCES

• The best way to keep the surfaces of kitchen appliances clean is to wipe them down after each use with a mixture of 3-percent hydrogen peroxide and warm water.

OVEN AND STOVETOP

• After using an oven's self-cleaning function, wipe down the interior surfaces with a cloth dipped in 3-percent hydrogen peroxide to collect any remaining debris.

• Remove baked-on crud from an oven with a paste of baking soda and hydrogen peroxide. Apply the paste, then scrub clean.

• To clean a stove exhaust hood, place paper towels or old newspaper below the hood to catch the grease as it runs off. Spray with hydrogen peroxide, followed by white vinegar, until completely saturated. Then wipe clean.

• When cleaning an oven, finish by wiping the entire surface with a sponge or clean cloth dipped in a mixture of equal parts warm water and hydrogen peroxide.

MICROWAVE

• Spray a few squirts of 3-percent hydrogen peroxide both inside and outside a microwave to clean it. Follow with a spray of white vinegar. Let the solutions sit a couple minutes, then wipe clean.

TOASTER OVEN

• Apply a paste of baking soda and 3-percent hydrogen peroxide to stubborn stains on a toaster oven's tray. Spray with white vinegar and let sit. Then wipe clean.

REFRIGERATOR

• Clear out all food items in the refrigerator before cleaning. Spray the interior walls and surfaces with undiluted 3-percent hydrogen peroxide. Follow with a spray of white vinegar. Leave the peroxide and vinegar on for at least 10 minutes before wiping with a clean cloth or paper towel.

• Give any removable drawers, bins, shelves, racks, or trays a bath with hot water and hydrogen peroxide to kill germs. Spray them with vinegar followed by hydrogen peroxide and wipe clean.

• Soak ice cube trays in warm water and hydrogen peroxide solution. Rinse thoroughly with clean water and air-dry.

DISHWASHER

• Load the automatic dishwasher as usual, but add a couple tablespoons of 3-percent hydrogen peroxide to your regular detergent to better clean and disinfect dishes.

• Occasionally run a cup or so of hydrogen peroxide through an empty dishwasher to remove mineral buildup, mildew, odors, and hard-water stains.

COFFEE MAKER

• Sporadically run about 1 cup of hydrogen peroxide through your coffee maker to keep it clean and disinfected. Rinse well with water before using the coffee maker again.

• Between cleanings, remove built-up coffee residue under the filtering apparatus with a clean cloth or sponge sprayed with hydrogen peroxide solution.

GARBAGE CANS AND DISPOSALS

• Disinfect the kitchen garbage can by spraying it with both your 3-percent hydrogen peroxide and vinegar solution bottles. Let sit for 10 minutes and then wipe clean.

• Periodically pour some baking soda and 3-percent hydrogen peroxide into your garbage disposal to kill germs and odors. Turn on hot water and run the garbage disposal for a few seconds to clean out debris and clear odors.

KITCHEN FLOORS

• For heavily soiled kitchen floors, combine 1 gallon of hot water and about 1 cup of hydrogen peroxide in a bucket. Mop the kitchen floors with this solution.

• For lighter jobs, mop kitchen floors with a basic solution of 1 gallon warm water and ⅛ cup hydrogen peroxide.

• Keep a spray bottle of 3-percent hydrogen peroxide handy for quick spot mopping. Spray the solution directly onto the affected area. Wait a few minutes and wipe clean. For especially greasy stains, allow the solution to penetrate longer before wiping. Repeat if necessary.

FRUITS AND VEGETABLES

• To remove bacteria and pesticides from fruit and vegetables, spray them with white vinegar, and then with hydrogen peroxide. Rinse thoroughly with cool water.

• Add a dash of salt and about ¼ cup 3-percent hydrogen peroxide to a clean sink full of cold water. Soak vegetables and fruits for several minutes, then rinse with cold water.

• Spray produce with a mixture of equal parts 3-percent hydrogen peroxide and water. Rinse with cold water.

Battling the Bathroom

The average person can tolerate a growing collection of dust balls beneath the bed, but a grimy bathroom is another story. If there's one cleaning job that must be done each week, it's cleaning the bathroom. Fortunately, hydrogen peroxide can help ensure you spend as little time, money, and elbow grease as possible keeping this all-important room comfortably clean.

GENERAL CLEANING

• Mix equal amounts of 3-percent hydrogen peroxide and water in a spray bottle, and use on bathroom surfaces for everyday maintenance.

• Remove mold and mildew from bathroom surfaces with a spray of 3-percent hydrogen peroxide solution. Allow solution to sit for 10 minutes, then wipe clean.

SOAP SCUM CLEANSER

Try this paste of cream of tartar and 3-percent hydrogen peroxide to remove soap scum buildup and calcium stains from the bathtub, sink, and surrounding tiles:

In a small container, mix just enough hydrogen peroxide into the cream of tartar to form a thick paste. Apply the paste directly onto the scummy surface, and scrub the surface with the paste. Then rinse clean and wipe dry.

• Clean ceramic tile countertops with a cloth dampened with 3-percent hydrogen peroxide.

• Remove a stain from a marble surface by mixing equal parts ammonia and hydrogen peroxide. Apply with a soft cloth. Wipe again with a cloth dampened with water.

SHOWERS AND TUBS

• Make your own daily shower spray by combining equal amounts of 3-percent hydrogen peroxide and water in a spray bottle. Spray the solution onto the bathtub or shower immediately after each use to fight off soap film and mildew. No need to rinse.

• Prevent mildew growth on a shower curtain by soaking it in a bath of hydrogen peroxide and water. Mix 1 part hydrogen peroxide and 4 parts warm water in the bathtub. Soak for at least 30 minutes, then rinse and hang to dry.

• Cover a stubborn bathtub ring with a paste made from cream of tartar and hydrogen peroxide. When the paste dries, wipe it off.

TOILETS

• Clean the toilet with 1 cup of hydrogen peroxide. Pour the undiluted 3-percent peroxide solution into the bowl, and let it sit for 20 minutes. Then scrub with a toilet brush and flush.

• Spray the toilet handle, seat, lid, tank, and any other exterior surfaces with 3-percent hydrogen peroxide. Wait for at least 10 minutes, then wipe with a clean cloth or paper towel.

• Disinfect the toilet brush between uses by spraying with your 3-percent hydrogen peroxide and white vinegar spray bottles.

TILE AND GROUT

• Remove small areas of mildew buildup on grout, caulk, or tile with undiluted 3-percent hydrogen peroxide solution. Dip a cloth into the peroxide and scrub.

• Use a paste of baking soda and 3-percent hydrogen peroxide to clean stubborn stains on tile and grout. Apply the paste, scrub with an old toothbrush, and rinse.

MIRRORS

• Use undiluted 3-percent hydrogen peroxide to give bathroom mirrors a streak-free shine. Spray the solution directly onto mirrors, and wipe with a clean cloth.

SINKS

• Brighten yellowed porcelain sinks by treating them with a paste of baking soda and 3-percent hydrogen peroxide.

• Attack stubborn rust stains in a sink with a paste of cream of tartar and hydrogen peroxide. Apply the paste, then scrub clean with a nonabrasive pad or brush. Rinse completely.

FAUCETS AND FIXTURES

• Discolored porcelain fixtures can be cleaned with a paste made of cream of tartar moistened with hydrogen peroxide. Scrub the paste into lightly stained areas with a brush, and rinse well.

• Use undiluted 3-percent hydrogen peroxide to combat lime buildup on your bathroom fixtures. Scrub, and rinse.

FLOORS

• For quick spot cleaning, just spray some undiluted 3-percent hydrogen peroxide onto bathroom floors and wipe clean.

Baby Care

Babies and toddlers may be little, but the challenges they present certainly aren't. Peroxide can help you deal with this bundle of challenges. Hydrogen peroxide offers an effective, inexpensive, and earth-friendly alternative to harsh chemicals like bleach, which can irritate the respiratory system. Because it breaks down into oxygen and water, hydrogen peroxide is better for your little one and the environment. From sanitizing sippy cups to cleaning cloth diapers, hydrogen peroxide is here help.

CLEAN, SANITIZE, AND DISINFECT

Sanitizing and disinfecting are usually two-step processes. Because sanitizers and disinfectants can't work on dirty or greasy surfaces, cleaning or pre-cleaning the surface is a necessary first step.

Clean: To physically remove dirt and debris that may act as a shield for bacteria and viruses from a surface by scrubbing, washing, and rinsing.

Sanitize: To reduce, but not necessarily eliminate, bacteria from the environment to a safe level.

Disinfect: To destroy or irreversibly inactivate infectious fungi and bacteria in the environment.

Ensure that your children are in another area when sanitizing or disinfecting. After the required contact time has lapsed, wipe surfaces dry. Make sure that all surfaces are dry before children return to the area.

• Sanitize a highchair tray by spraying undiluted 3-percent hydrogen peroxide. Allow the solution to sit undisturbed for at least 10 minutes. Then wipe with a clean cloth or paper towel.

• **Tip:** When 3-percent hydrogen peroxide solution is heated to at least 130°F, it can sanitize a surface after only 1 minute of contact time.

• Use a solution of 1½ cups hydrogen peroxide per gallon of water to sponge down a highchair. Let the solution stand for 10–15 minutes, rinse, and air-dry.

• To sanitize baby bottles, first wash with hot soapy water and rinse. Spray 3-percent hydrogen peroxide into the bottles and let sit 10 minutes. Then rinse well with water and drain bottles upside down.

• Sanitize pacifiers, teething rings, baby bottles, sippy cups, and feeding spoons with hydrogen peroxide. First prewash the items in hot soapy water. Then soak the items in a bath of hydrogen peroxide for a minimum of 10 minutes. Pour the solution through any bottle nipples. Rinse all items well, drain, and air-dry.

• A similar method can be used to disinfect rubber ducks, toy keys, and other plastic items babies frequently put in their mouths. Soak the prewashed playthings in undiluted 3-percent hydrogen peroxide solution for 20 minutes.

• Diaper changing tables and potty training chairs should be cleaned regularly with white vinegar and 3-percent hydrogen peroxide. Spray surfaces with vinegar, followed by hydrogen peroxide. Wait 10 minutes, then wipe both solutions from surfaces with a clean paper towel.

• It's not pretty, but it happens—babies go to the bathroom in tubs. When this occurs, spray distilled white vinegar, followed by 3-percent hydrogen peroxide, to disinfect the tub. Allow at least 10 minutes of contact time, then wipe with a clean cloth or paper towel.

• Wipe crib and playpen rails with 3-percent hydrogen peroxide and allow to air-dry.

• Spray undiluted 3-percent hydrogen peroxide on play area surfaces, wait a few minutes, then simply wipe clean.

• Sanitize mouthed surfaces on cribs or playpens by spraying undiluted 3-percent hydrogen peroxide. Leave the hydrogen peroxide on for 10 minutes, then wipe with a clean cloth.

TOTS AND TOYS

• Cloth toys can get grungy. To clean soft toys in a washing machine, add a little bit of hydrogen peroxide to the load to kill germs.

• Clean vinyl toys with a solution of equal parts hydrogen peroxide and water. Wash toys with a damp cloth, rinse, and dry.

• To disinfect plastic toys, first clean them with hot soapy water and rinse. Then soak the toys in a bath of 3-percent hydrogen peroxide for 20 minutes.

• Eliminate germs from playroom surfaces with white vinegar and hydrogen peroxide. Spray one and then the other. Wipe clean after 10 minutes.

BABY LAUNDRY

• Use hydrogen peroxide as a bleach alternative when laundering crib bedding, changing table linens, and cloth diapers.

• For urine-drenched bedding, presoak in 3-percent hydrogen peroxide solution with some baking soda added. Then launder bedding as usual.

• For cleaner cloth diapers, add a cup or two of 3-percent hydrogen peroxide solution to your washing machine for each load of soiled diapers.

• For tough stains on baby clothes, soak the items (colorfast only) in a bucket of water with ½ cup hydrogen peroxide added. Wait 10 minutes, rinse in clean water, then launder as usual. Repeat if necessary.

Home Remedies

Hydrogen peroxide isn't just for cleaning your kitchen or removing laundry stains. That cheap brown bottle of hydrogen peroxide can help relieve athlete's foot, soothe a sore throat, clean minor cuts, prevent gum disease, alleviate aches and pains, and more. Of course, the advice given here is meant to supplement—not replace—professional medical advice. Nevertheless, the healing and pain-relieving properties of hydrogen peroxide are remarkable.

MIND YOUR MOUTH

• Prevent gum disease by brushing your teeth with a paste made from 3 parts baking soda and 1 part hydrogen peroxide.

• Gargle with a solution of 3-percent hydrogen peroxide and water to keep your mouth and gums healthy. Dilute hydrogen peroxide with an equal amount of water, and swish around your mouth for 30 seconds. Don't swallow the rinse.

• **Tip:** A solution stronger than 3 percent is dangerous. Hydrogen peroxide rids the mouth of food particles, and the oxygenating agent helps boost the fighting properties of good bacteria.

• Canker sores are painful and annoying, but you can ease the pain and promote healing with hydrogen peroxide. Dip a cotton swab in 3-percent hydrogen peroxide solution and hold it against the sore for a minute or so. Then rinse your mouth with water.

• Here is another canker sore remedy: Mix a solution of half 3-percent hydrogen peroxide and half water. Swish the 50/50 solution around in your mouth every few hours until the canker sore heals.

• After biting your tongue or cheek, rinse with a solution of equal parts 3-percent hydrogen peroxide and water. This rinse can help with other irritating mouth ailments as well.

FIXES FOR YOUR FEET

• Relieve athlete's foot by soaking feet in a warm bath of hydrogen peroxide. Fill a basin with warm water and add about ½ cup hydrogen peroxide. Soak feet in the solution for 10 minutes once or twice a day.

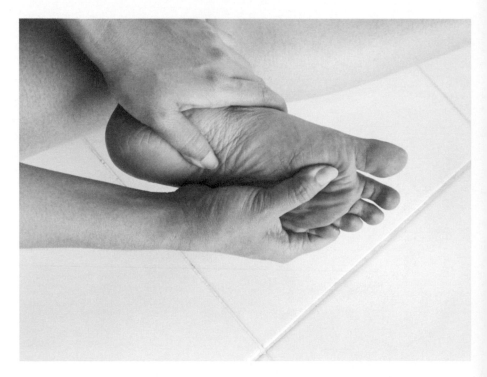

• Spraying the shower stall or bathtub with undiluted 3-percent hydrogen peroxide after each use will help kill fungi and reduce the risk of future foot problems.

• Blisters can also benefit from a hydrogen peroxide bath. Soak blistered feet in a solution of warm water and 3-percent hydrogen peroxide for several minutes. Rinse feet and pat dry.

SKIN SOLUTIONS

• After removing a splinter, clean the wound with soap and water, then pour a little hydrogen peroxide on the area to clean out any remaining debris and speed healing.

• Wet a cotton ball with 3-percent hydrogen peroxide and dab it onto minor rashes.

MINOR CUTS AND SCRAPES

• Try cleaning minor cuts, scrapes, and abrasions with undiluted 3-percent hydrogen peroxide. After rinsing with water, pour the hydrogen peroxide directly onto the affected area and allow the solution to fizz on the surface. Rinse with water again and bandage if necessary.

• **Tip:** Never use hydrogen peroxide to treat deep-tissue wounds, as it can slow the healing process.

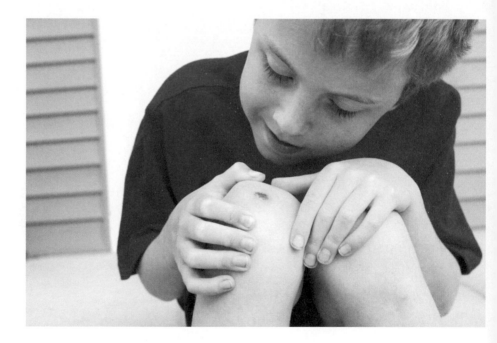

BUG BITES AND STINGS

• Dampen a cotton ball with 3-percent hydrogen peroxide and dab the mosquito bite.

• Treat bug bites and stings with 3-percent hydrogen peroxide. Pour or spray the undiluted solution directly onto the affected area.

• Apply hydrogen peroxide to minor animal bites or scratches to kill germs.

ALLERGIES AND ASTHMA

• Ease breathing difficulties for allergy and asthma sufferers by adding 3-percent hydrogen peroxide to the humidifier or vaporizer. Add about 2 cups per gallon of water.

• **Tip:** Keep humidifiers and vaporizers circulating hydrogen peroxide away from delicate walls, curtains, and furniture, as mild bleaching could occur.

EARS, NOSE, AND THROAT

• Gargle (but don't swallow) with 3-percent hydrogen peroxide a few times a day to ease a sore throat.

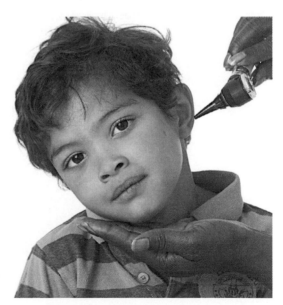

• Relieve ear pain with a few drops of 3-percent hydrogen peroxide. Tilt head to the side and administer the hydrogen peroxide to the affected ear. Allow the solution to fizz and bubble for a few seconds. Then tilt your head and empty the solution onto a tissue or cotton ball.

• To help with sinus congestion and pressure, fill an empty nasal pump or inhaler with a solution of half water and half 3-percent hydrogen peroxide. Spray the solution into your nostrils and then blow out to clear congestion.

ACHES AND PAINS

• To soothe arthritis pain in your feet, add about 1 cup of 3-percent hydrogen peroxide and 2 tablespoons Epsom salts to a tub of warm water. Soak painful feet for 15 minutes, rinse, and pat dry.

Beauty and Grooming

Look and feel your best from head to toe with help from hydrogen peroxide. Hydrogen peroxide is a wonderful—and inexpensive—addition to your beauty regimens. It can help clear up skin problems, lighten hair, and brighten your smile. Read on for even more beauty tips that will help you stay beautiful without spending a fortune.

THE SKINNY ON SKIN
Banish Blemishes
• Hydrogen peroxide can help combat acne. For spot relief, use a cotton swab dipped in 3-percent hydrogen peroxide.

• Apply hydrogen peroxide to acne breakouts and leave on overnight. In the morning, rinse your face with cool water.

• Prevent acne breakouts by swabbing your face with hydrogen peroxide on a cotton ball or tissue twice a week.

Spot Check

• Bothered by freckles and age spots? Apply hydrogen peroxide to each spot with a cotton ball. Repeat every few days until spots have lightened to your liking. Try alternating hydrogen peroxide and lemon juice.

• Another trick to lighten the effects of age and the sun: Dip a cotton swab in 3-percent hydrogen peroxide and dab it onto age spots or freckles before bed. Allow to air-dry. Rinse your face with cool water in the morning.

TEETH AND TEETH TOOLS

• Make your own whitening toothpaste by mixing 1 teaspoon of baking soda and ½ teaspoon of 3-percent hydrogen peroxide into a paste. Use immediately to brush and whiten teeth. Do not swallow. This homemade toothpaste quickly loses effectiveness, so it's best to make it in small batches.

• For coffee stains between teeth, try soaking dental floss in 3-percent hydrogen peroxide before flossing. Then gargle with a mixture of 4 parts water to 1 part 3-percent hydrogen peroxide after flossing for improved whitening.

• Disinfect your toothbrush by soaking it in hydrogen peroxide. Pour undiluted 3-percent hydrogen peroxide into a small cup or dish and drop your toothbrush in on its head. Soak for at least 20 minutes, then rinse with cold water.

• Occasionally soak retainers and dental appliances in a solution of hydrogen peroxide and water.

Care for (Unwanted) Hair

• Looking for a low-cost way to lighten upper lip hair? Combine 1 teaspoon ammonia and ¼ cup hydrogen peroxide. Dab the mixture on upper lip area with a cotton ball and leave on for 30 minutes. Rinse off with cold water.

Nail Care

• Try brightening your fingernails and toenails in a hydrogen peroxide bath. Combine equal parts warm water and 3-percent hydrogen peroxide. Soak nails for 10 minutes, then rinse well with warm water.

Laundry and Clothing Care

You can tackle a laundry list of troublesome stains with hydrogen peroxide. The 3-percent hydrogen peroxide solution sold at drugstores is tough on stains, but tender on delicate fabrics like silk. Hydrogen peroxide works to freshen, clean, and whiten your laundry and is safer than chlorine bleach for virtually all washable fabrics.

STAINS BE GONE!

Blood

• Clean a fresh bloodstain with 3-percent hydrogen peroxide. Dab on the peroxide, then blot off, repeating as necessary. Test a hidden area first to be sure the fabric is colorfast.

STORING AND USING HYDROGEN PEROXIDE

The 3-percent hydrogen peroxide solution sold in drugstores has mild antiseptic and bleaching effects. It is safe for most fibers, though it's always best to spot-test in a hidden area. (The higher-percent, more potent peroxide solution used for lightening hair is too strong to use safely on fabric and other household surfaces.) Buy hydrogen peroxide in small quantities and store it in a cool, dark place in its original opaque container; it loses strength quickly after it is opened and if it is exposed to light.

• For dried bloodstains on clothing, soak the stain with 3-percent hydrogen peroxide, use your fingernail or the blade of a butter knife to help loosen and scrape away the blood, then rinse it away with more hydrogen peroxide.

Grass
• Use 3-percent hydrogen peroxide solution on stubborn grass stains. Then thoroughly rinse with clear water, and launder as usual.

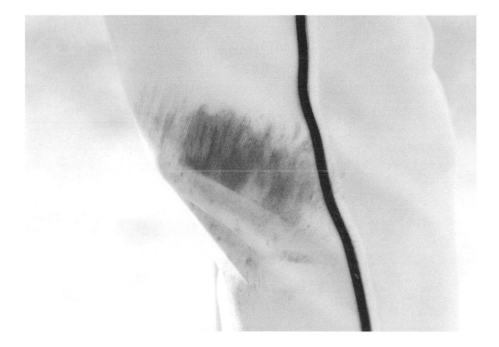

Mustard
• Mustard contains turmeric, a yellow dye. Mustard stains not treated immediately can be impossible to remove. Moisten the mustard-stained area with 3-percent hydrogen peroxide and a drop of ammonia (do not use ammonia on

silk or wool). The bleaching solution should not remain on the stain for longer than 15 minutes. Flush with water and allow to dry.

• Here's another technique for treating mustard stains: Place a cloth soaked in hydrogen peroxide over the stain, then an ammonia-soaked cloth over that. Leave in place until stain has faded, sponge with water, and pat dry. Sunlight may help further fade the mustard stain.

Ink

• Some ink stains respond to a solution of 2 teaspoons of 3-percent hydrogen peroxide in 1 cup of water. Test for colorfastness first! Spray solution onto stain or apply with a cotton swab.

COLORFASTNESS

Colorfast fabric retains its original color without bleeding, running, or fading. Before using bleaching solutions such as hydrogen peroxide on colored fabrics, you should test for colorfastness. Mix 1 tablespoon of hydrogen peroxide with 2 quarts of hot water. Apply this solution to an inconspicuous area, like an interior seam. Dab the area with a clean white cloth. If any color comes off onto the white cloth, the item is not colorfast and you should not use hydrogen peroxide on the fabric.

HOMEMADE STAIN SPRAY

To pretreat a tough stain before washing, try this homemade stain-removal spray:

½ cup rubbing alcohol
½ cup hydrogen peroxide
¼ cup clear dishwashing liquid
¼ cup water

Add all ingredients to a spray bottle, and shake well before use.

Red Wine
• For red wine stains, try cleaning with 3-percent hydrogen peroxide. Dab on the peroxide, then blot off. Repeat if necessary.

Perspiration
• Perspiration stains can sometimes be removed from clothing with hydrogen peroxide. Spray hydrogen peroxide solution onto stains, and then wait 10 minutes before laundering.

Stains on Silk
• Silk requires special care. To remove stains from washable white or light-colored silk, use a mix of 1 part 3-percent hydrogen peroxide to 8 parts water.

Yellowing
• Old linens, curtains, and tablecloths can yellow over time. To brighten yellowed linens, add ½ cup of 3-percent hydrogen peroxide to 1 gallon of water. Soak the yellowed fabric for an hour, then launder as usual.

Scorch Marks
• Scorch marks—the bane of anyone who irons—don't have to destroy your white clothes. Spray the scorch marks with hydrogen peroxide, cover with a white cloth, and iron again. Like magic, the scorch marks should disappear.

The Great
Outdoors

We've already seen dozens of uses for hydrogen peroxide inside your home. Now learn about the many ways to use hydrogen peroxide outside, too! Hydrogen peroxide is a great alternative to toxic chemicals for gardening, cleaning, and outdoor maintenance projects. Beyond the backyard, hydrogen peroxide can work wonders with your car.

YOUR GREEN THUMB

• Clean used pots before you use them for new plants with a solution of 1 part hydrogen peroxide to 6 parts water. Soak for 15 minutes. Rinse and dry.

• Extend the life of freshly cut flowers by adding ¼ teaspoon of 3-percent hydrogen peroxide to the vase.

• Give seedlings a head start by soaking them overnight in a solution of 1 tablespoon of 3-percent hydrogen peroxide and 1 cup of water. Then plant seedlings as usual.

• Try this fertilizer spray for garden plants: Mix 2 tablespoons of 3-percent hydrogen peroxide in 1 gallon of water. Pour liquid into a watering can or garden sprayer. Use solution on garden plants and surrounding soil.

• Spray garden flowers with a solution made of 4 cups of water and 2 tablespoons of 3-percent hydrogen peroxide to encourage growth.

• For diseased plants, mix a solution of 1 cup of 3-percent hydrogen peroxide and 1 gallon of water. Pour solution into a spray bottle, and spray affected plants.

• Plant diseases can be as contagious as human varieties. Immediately after working with discased plants, clean your garden tools in a mixture of 1 part 3-percent hydrogen peroxide to 3 parts water.

BACKYARD TIPS

Patios
• Attack mildew on plastic patio furniture with hydrogen peroxide. Add 1 cup of 3-percent hydrogen peroxide per gallon of water, test for colorfastness on a hidden spot, and then scrub away. Rinse well with clear water. Let the pieces dry completely before storing.

• Clean moss and stains on concrete patios with a solution of ¾ cup of hydrogen peroxide per gallon of water. Pour some on the affected area and wait 10 minutes. Scrub with a strong-bristled brush. Rinse well.

Birdbaths
• Clean a cement birdbath with 3-percent hydrogen peroxide to keep algae and bacteria at bay. Empty the birdbath and allow to dry completely. Pour undiluted hydrogen peroxide into the birdbath and wait 1 hour. Scrub with a sturdy brush until clean. Rinse well with clear water and then refill the birdbath.

CARE FOR YOUR CAR
• Clean your car windows with undiluted 3-percent hydrogen peroxide. Spray the solution onto interior or exterior car windows, then wipe with a clean cloth.

• **Tip:** Leave car doors open while spraying interior windows with hydrogen peroxide.

• Spray 3-percent hydrogen peroxide onto vinyl and plastic car interiors, and then wipe with a clean cloth dampened with water.

Caring for Creatures

Pet owners know their little friends can be enchanting (and exasperating), companionable (and costly), and wonderful (and worrisome). But we can turn to hydrogen peroxide in our quest to care for and clean up after our creatures. These pet tips and ideas are meant to complement—never replace—professional veterinarian care.

CARE FOR FURRY FRIENDS

• Your furry friend deserves germ-free food and water. To disinfect your pet's food and water bowls, mix 2 tablespoons of 3-percent hydrogen peroxide into 1 gallon of water. Soak the prewashed bowls in the solution for at least 20 minutes, then drain, rinse, and air-dry.

• Clean plastic carrying cases with a solution of equal parts hydrogen peroxide and water. Spray cases thoroughly, wait 10 minutes, then wipe dry.

• If your pet has a run-in with a skunk, wash the pet in a bath containing 1 quart of 3-percent hydrogen peroxide, ¼ cup baking soda, and 1 teaspoon liquid dish soap. Rinse well and dry. Discard unused cleaner.

• Disinfect your cat litter scoop in a bath of hydrogen peroxide. Soak the litter scoop in 3-percent hydrogen peroxide solution for 20 minutes.

EAR-CLEANING SOLUTION

Try this ear-cleaning solution for your cats and dogs:

1 tablespoon 3-percent hydrogen peroxide
1 tablespoon vinegar
1 tablespoon yucca root tea
1 drop lavender oil
½ cup aloe vera gel

Mix ingredients and apply to your pet's ears with cotton swabs.

• To prevent ear mites, regularly swab your pet's ears with cotton balls saturated in 3-percent hydrogen peroxide. Then wipe away excess liquid with clean, dry cotton balls.

CARE FOR BIRDS

• Spray your bird's cage with hydrogen peroxide and wipe clean. Dry metal cages thoroughly to prevent rusting.

• Sanitize water trays and dishes for your bird by soaking in a solution of 1 part hydrogen peroxide to 4 parts water. Do not soak metal trays and dishes.

CARE FOR FISH

• Clean aquarium accessories in a bowl of water with 1 teaspoon of 3-percent hydrogen peroxide added. Soak for 10 minutes, then rinse well before returning to the tank.